Across the Fence

THEODORE CLYMER
RICHARD L. VENEZKY

Consultants
CLAIRE HENRY
DALE D. JOHNSON
HUGHES MOIR
P. DAVID PEARSON
PHYLLIS WEAVER

Ginn and Company

0-663-38545-8

Acknowledgments: Grateful acknowledgment is
made to the following publishers, authors, and
agents for permission to use and adapt copyrighted
material:

American Folklore Society for "How Little Lamb
Fooled Señor Coyote" by Verna Aardema. Retold
and translated by permission of the American
Folklore Society from *Tales from Jalisco Mexico,
1943.*

Andre Deutsch Limited, London, for "The
Bear's Bicycle," abridged, with selected
illustrations, from *The Bear's Bicycle* by Emilie
Warren McLeod, illustrated by David McPhail. Text
copyright © 1975 by Emilie Warren McLeod.
Illustrations copyright © 1975 by David McPhail.
Used by permission of the British publisher.

Harper & Row, Publishers, Inc., for the adapted
text and art of "A New House" from *Grasshopper on
the Road,* written and illustrated by Arnold Lobel.
Copyright © 1978 by Arnold Lobel. By permission of
Harper & Row, Publishers, Inc., and of World's Work
Ltd, England. Also for the adapted text and art of
"The Surprise" from *Frog and Toad All Year,* written
and illustrated by Arnold Lobel. Copyright © 1976 by
Arnold Lobel. An *I Can Read* Book. By permission of
Harper & Row, Publishers, Inc., and of World's Work
Ltd, England.

George G. Harrap & Company Limited, London,
for the poem "Every Time I Climb a Tree," abridged
from *Mr. Bidery's Spidery Garden* by David McCord.
Used by permission of the British publisher.

Little, Brown and Company for "The Bear's
Bicycle," abridged, with selected illustrations, from
The Bear's Bicycle by Emilie Warren McLeod,
illustrated by David McPhail. Text copyright © 1975
by Emilie Warren McLeod. Illustrations copyright ©
1975 by David McPhail. By permission of Little,
Brown and Company in association with the Atlantic
Monthly Press. Also for the play "Chicken Forgets,"
adapted from *Chicken Forgets* by Miska Miles. Text

copyright © 1976 by Miska Miles. By permission of
Little, Brown and Company in association with the
Atlantic Monthly Press. Also for the poem "Every
Time I Climb a Tree," abridged from *Far and Few* by
David McCord. Copyright © 1952 by David McCord.
By permission of Little, Brown and Company.

Macmillan Publishing Co., Inc., for "Sea Frog,
City Frog" by Dorothy Van Woerkom. Adapted with
permission of Macmillan Publishing Co., Inc. from
Sea Frog, City Frog by Dorothy O. Van Woerkom.
Copyright © 1975 by Dorothy O. Van Woerkom.

G. P. Putnam's Sons for the peom "Blum" by
Dorothy Aldis. Reprinted by permission of G. P.
Putnam's Sons from *Here There & Everywhere* by
Dorothy Aldis. Copyright 1927, 1928; renewed ©
1955, 1956 by Dorothy Aldis.

Viking Penguin Inc. for the poem "A House Is a
House for Me," which is a selection from *A House Is
a House for Me* by Mary Ann Hoberman. Copyright
© 1978 by Mary Ann Hoberman. Reprinted by
permission of Viking Penguin Inc.

Frederick Warne & Co., Ltd., London, for
selected illustrations from the publications of
Beatrix Potter and the excerpt from her letter, all
included in "Who Is Beatrix Potter?" © Copyright F.
Warne and Co. Ltd., London. Used by permission of
the publisher.

Illustrators and Photographers: Peter Bradford,
cover, 6-7, 50-51, 86-87, 108-109, 126-127; William
McDade, 1-5, 48, 84-85, 125, 166-167; Kevin Young,
6-7, 50-51, 86-87, 126-127; James Marshall, 8-15;
Bob Shein, 16-29; Yoshi Miyake, 30-37; Carolyn
McHenry, 38-49, 54-59; Judy Pelikan, 52-53;
Jacqueline Chwast, 60-67; Arnold Lobel, 68-75, 110-
119; Susan Spellman Mohn, 76-85; Cathy Bennett,
88-95; Bernard LaCasse, 96-99; Sandy Schafer, 96-
99; Michael L. Pateman, 100-107; Ray Komai, 120-
124; Beatrix Potter, 128-135; Mary Anne McLean,
136-145; Doug Cushman, 146-155; Diane
Palmisciano, 156-167; David McPhail, 168-189.

Design, Ginn Reading Program:
Creative Director: Peter Bradford
Art Director: Gary Fujiwara
Design Coordinator: Anne Todd
Design: Lorraine Johnson, Linda Post, Kevin
Young, Cathy Bennett, Kristen Dietrich

Contents

Unit 3   WHAT DO YOU SAY?   86

Fin

You will read about new ways to do things.
First you will meet a hen who finds a way
to get some help.

Let's see who the hen finds to help her.

ding
a
Way

7

Help for the Hen

James Marshall

" Good day, " said a hen to a dog.
" I need some help at my house.
Could you help me ? "

" I can't help you now, " said the dog.
" The day is too beautiful. Why don't you
ask that cat ? "

" Very well, " said the hen. " I will. "

" What do you want ? " asked the cat.

" I need some help at my house, "
said the hen. " Could you help me ? "

" That's the last thing I want to do on a day
like this, " said the cat. " Maybe that frog
will help. "

" Maybe so, " said the hen.

"How do you do?" said the hen to the frog. "Will you help me?"

"I'm afraid not," said the frog. "I'm going to take a swim. Ask that duck down the way. She has very little to do."

"I'll do that," said the hen.

" Will you give me some help ? "
asked the hen.

The duck said, " I can't help you.
I have three ducklings to take care of.
Ask that bird. He must have little to do. "

" I hope so, " said the hen.

11

The hen flew up into a big tree.

" I know, I know, " said the bird.

" You need some help. "

" Will you help me ? " asked the hen.

" I can't, " said the bird.

" I'm going to see my grandma.

Why don't you go ask that fox ? "

" A fox ? " asked the hen.

12

The hen was afraid.

But she did need help.

"Fox," she said. "I need some help."

"I'll be happy to help," said the fox.

"You will?" asked the hen.

13

Everyone wanted to know what the fox and the hen were doing.

"It's a trick," said the cat.

"He's going to eat her," said the duck.

"That's the last we'll see of her," said the frog.

14

They all looked across the fence at
the hen and the fox.

"I couldn't eat them all by myself,"
said the hen.

"I am very happy to help," said the fox.

Bones, Bones, Bones

Ned Delaney

Dog looked at the floor in his kitchen.
" I can't see the floor. All I can see are bones.
This place is getting to be a mess, " he said.

Dog looked for his dishes. He could not
find the dishes in his kitchen. All the dishes
were filled with bones. " Bones! Bones!
Everyone likes to give me bones! " he said.
" These bones are getting in my way.
I'll have to do something about this. "

Dog went to find Duck, Fox, and Bear.

" My friends will help me, " he thought.

Dog found his friends swimming in the pond.

" Would you like to play a game ? " Dog asked.

" Yes, we like to play games ! " they cried.

" Come to my house, " said Dog.

" We will play a game, and then I will make us a good lunch. "

They all ran to Dog's house.

" Look at all the bones ! " Fox cried.

" This place is a mess, " said Bear.

" What game are we going to play ? " asked Duck.

" I call it Bone-in-a-Hole. First, you must dig some holes. Then we will put all these bones in the holes . "

" That is not a game, " Duck said. " Digging a hole is work. It's no fun ! "

" Don't go, " cried Dog. " If you help me, I will make you a good lunch. "

" No ! " said Duck, Fox, and Bear.

Then back they went to the pond.

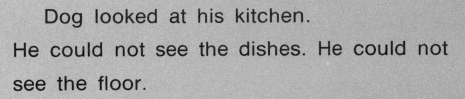

Dog looked at his kitchen.
He could not see the dishes. He could not
see the floor.

" This place is getting to be a mess, "
he said. " What will I do ? "

Then Dog thought, " I could ask Owl what
to do. She may know where I can
put these bones. "

Dog ran to see Owl.

"Owl, everyone likes to give me bones,"
he said. "My dishes are filled with bones.
My kitchen is filled with bones.
My house is getting to be a mess.
Owl, what can I do?"

Owl thought and thought.

"Dog," she said, "I know how you can get rid of the bones. Come here. Do you see that red house?"

Dog looked. "Yes, I see it," he said.

"In back of that house, some dogs are making something big out of bones," Owl said. "They need a lot of bones to make it. I know they would like your bones."

Dog ran to the pond where his friends were swimming.

" Come to my house, " he said.
" I have another way to get rid of the bones. You do not have to dig a hole.
If you will help me, I will make you a good lunch. Bear, we need your big truck. "

So Duck, Fox, and Bear went to Dog's house. Dog and his friends put all the bones in Bear's truck. They took them to the red house.

" How do you like what we are making ? " asked the dogs.

" It's great ! " said Dog and his friends.

" Come to my house now, " said Dog,
" and I will make us a good lunch. "

Dog's friends went back to his house.
Dog made some lunch and took out his dishes.

" What is this ? " they cried. " Not bones ! "

" Yes, " said Dog. " The dogs at the
red house gave me some very good bones.
I thought they would be great for lunch. "

" Oh, no ! " said Dog's friends.
" Bones for lunch ? "

" Forget lunch ! " Bear said.
" I'm going swimming. "

Duck, Fox, and Bear got up, and they
went back to the pond.

" They don't know a good lunch when they
see one ! " thought Dog.

Some of This and Some of That
Laurie Siegel

What do you need to build something?
The first thing you need is a plan. A builder
makes a plan of what she wants to build.
The plan is a picture of what she will build.

Now there is a plan.

You will need some tools, too.

Here are some tools you could use.

Here are some ways to use these tools.

25

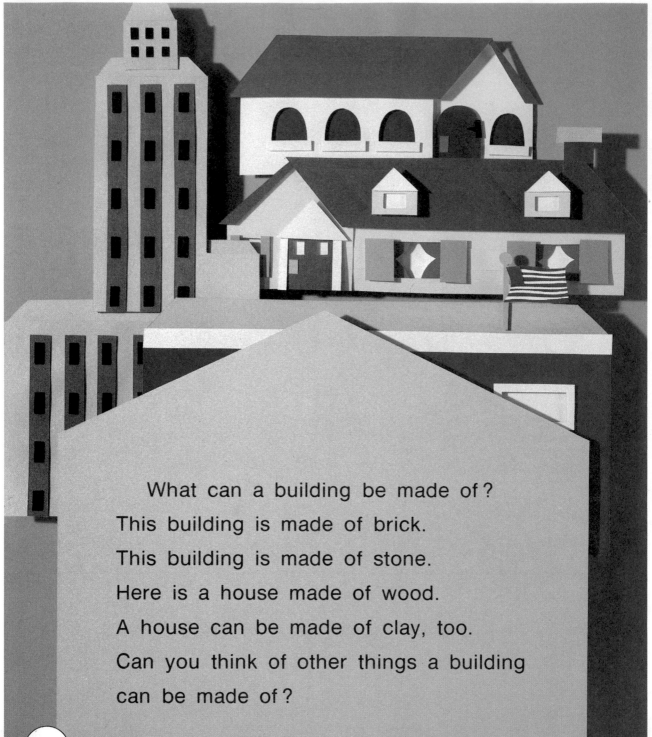

What can a building be made of?

This building is made of brick.

This building is made of stone.

Here is a house made of wood.

A house can be made of clay, too.

Can you think of other things a building

can be made of?

26

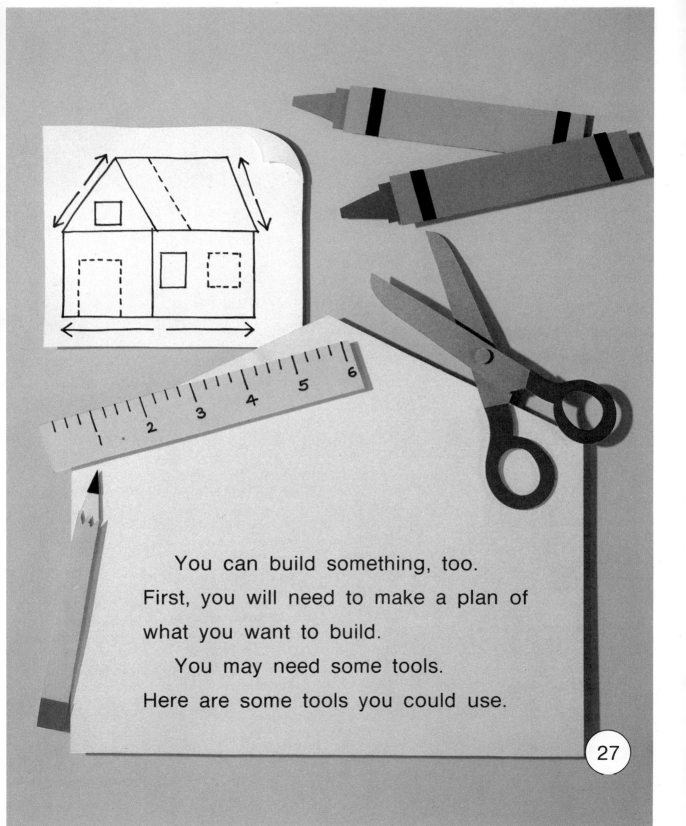

You can build something, too.

First, you will need to make a plan of what you want to build.

You may need some tools.

Here are some tools you could use.

What will you use to make your building?
You do not have to use brick or wood.
You may not have stone or clay.
Here are some things you could use.

You don't have to make something you
have seen. Maybe you will make
something no one has ever made.
Will it be something big or little?
You are the only one who can say.

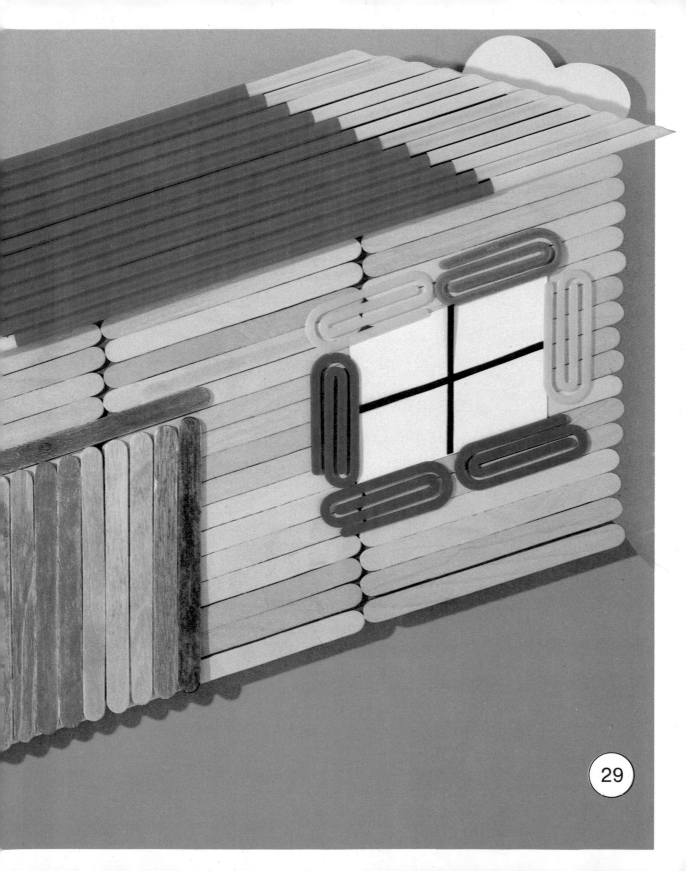

Give Us a Clue   Walker Stewart

Tim lives one house away from my house. He likes to come to my house around lunch time. Maybe you know someone like that.

One day, Tim and I were talking about what to do after lunch.

" What do you want to do ? " I asked.

" I don't know, " said Tim.
" What do you want to do ? "

Dad could hear us talking.

" Hello, Tim, " Dad said. " It's nice to see you. "

" Dad, we are looking for something to do, " I said. " Do you know something we can do by ourselves ? "

" Well, " he said, " maybe I can help you. Come see me after you eat lunch. I have to do something first. "

After we had lunch, we went to see Dad.

" Hello again, " Dad said. " I have something which you may want to do. I made up some clues for you to read. First you will read the clues. Then you will go where the clues tell you to go. You will find another clue there. Go from clue to clue. The last clue will take you to something you will like. "

" Can we read the clues by ourselves? " I asked.

" Yes, you can, " said Dad.

Dad gave me the first clue. It said:

 I'm very tall.

 Some of me is up in the air.

 A bird can come home to me.

 What am I?

" It has to be something big, " said Tim.

" The clue said some of it was up in the air. "

" The clue said it was very tall, too, " I said.

" Where would a bird go home? " asked Tim.

" A bird would go home to a tree, " I said.

" It can only be a tree! Come on! "

We knew it had to be a tree.

But which tree was it?

Which tree could it be?

First we ran to the tree by the road.

We looked up in the air. We looked

all around that tree. The clue was not there.

So we went to another tree.

"Here's the clue!" said Tim. "I'll read it."

You can see me on the road.

But I can't see you.

I'm very big and have wheels.

What am I?

We knew it was something that could
go on a road.

"Maybe it's a bike," said Tim.

"It can't be a bike, silly!" I said.
"A bike is not very big. A van and
a train are very big, and they have wheels."

"A train can't go on a road," said Tim.

"Well, we don't have a van," I said.
"We only have a truck."

"That's it! A truck!" said Tim.

Tim and I ran to the truck.

The clue was there! I read the clue to Tim.

I have pink eyes.

My ears are long.

I'm nice to hold.

I'm on the kitchen floor.

" What could it be ? " I asked.

" Maybe it's a donkey, " said Tim.

" A donkey has long ears. "

" A donkey is not nice to hold, " I said.

" Could it be a kitten ? A kitten is nice to hold. "

" A kitten does not have pink eyes, " said Tim.

" A rabbit has pink eyes, " I said. " A
rabbit is nice to hold, and it has long ears ! "

" That's it ! " said Tim. " The rabbit must
be on the kitchen floor ! "

We ran into the house.

A little, white rabbit was on the kitchen floor!

"Hello again," said Dad.

"I see you found all the clues."

"We found the rabbit all by ourselves!" I said.

"This rabbit was for your birthday," said Dad. "Mom and I knew you would like to have it now."

"The rabbit is great, Dad!" I said. "Come on, Tim. This rabbit needs something to eat."

"He's not the only one who needs something to eat," said Tim.

Puff

Lynne S. Forman

Puff was Sue's dog.

Sue thought Puff was a great dog.

Sue thought Puff was a nice dog.

Sue thought Puff was a fine dog.

Sue's friends thought Puff was a big pest.

Puff went where Sue went.

That was fine with Sue, but it was not
fine with her friends.

Some of Sue's friends were afraid of Puff.

They didn't like the way Puff kissed them.

They didn't like the way Puff jumped on
top of them.

" Puff is getting in the way, " they said.
" We can't play with you if Puff is around. "

39

" Listen, Puff, " said Sue.

" If you keep this up, I'll have no friends.

Some of my friends are afraid of you.

They don't know how nice you are.

They don't like it when you kiss them.

They don't like it when you

jump on top of them.

I thought of a way to get my friends back.

I hope it will be OK with you. "

Sue was making something to get her friends back. She had to work all day to make it.

"I can't wait for my friends to see what I have made," she thought.

"I know my friends will like this."

41

Sue went down the road to find her friends.

" Hello, Jack, " said Sue.

" Will you play with me ? "

" No, " said Jack.

" You know that I'm afraid of Puff. "

" You don't have to be afraid now, "
said Sue. " I know where
we can play by ourselves. "

" Did you give Puff away ? " asked Jack.

" No, I did not give Puff away, " said Sue.
" Come to my house. You don't have to
be afraid. "

Sue went down the road to find Gail.

" Hello, Gail, " said Sue.

" Will you play with me ? "

" No, I will not play with you, " said Gail.
" I don't like it when Puff wants to kiss me. "

" Puff will not kiss you now, " said Sue.
" I have found a way that we can
play by ourselves. Come to my house.
You will see that it's OK. "

43

Then Sue found Peg.

" Hello, Peg, " said Sue.

" Will you play with me ? "

" No, I don't want to play with you, "
said Peg. " I don't like it
when Puff jumps on top of me. "

" Puff will not jump on you now, "
said Sue. " I have found a way that we can
play by ourselves. Come to my house.
You'll see what I mean. "

All of Sue's friends came to her house.

They didn't know what happened to Puff.

They found out that Puff was the same.
But Sue had made a great place to play.
Now Puff could not make them afraid.
Puff could not kiss them here.
Puff could not jump on top of them.

" Sue, this tree house is a great
place to play! " said Peg. " Puff looks like
a very nice dog from here. "

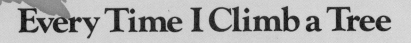

Every Time I Climb a Tree

Every time I climb a tree

Every time I climb a tree

Every time I climb a tree

I scrape a leg

Or skin a knee

And every time I climb a tree

I find some ants

Or dodge a bee

And get the ants

All over me

Though climbing may be good for ants

It isn't awfully good for pants

But still it's pretty good for me

Every time I climb a tree

David McCord

Yes, No, Maybe?

Is he in a rush?

Will a chick like this lunch?

Will they need a bath?

What's It All About?

We all need a place to live.
You will read about:
  someone who lives in an apple,
  someone who lives in a den,
  someone who lives in the water.
First we will look out some windows.
Let's see what there is to see.

All Around Us

A House Is a House for Me

A hill is a house for an ant, an ant.
A hive is a house for a bee.
A hole is a house for a mole or a mouse
And a house is a house for me!

A web is a house for a spider.
A bird builds its nest in a tree.
There is nothing so snug as a bug in a rug
And a house is a house for me!

A book is a house for a story.
A rose is a house for a smell.
My head is a house for a secret,
A secret I never will tell.

A flower's at home in a garden.
A donkey's at home in a stall.
Each creature that's known
    has a house of its own
And the earth is a house for us all.

Mary Ann Hoberman

53

A Window Here,
A Window There Merle Greene

Can you tell where this house is?

Look out the window. What do you see?

The trees are old. Do you see
something new on these trees?

A dog is lying in the sun.

Do you see him lying by the pond?

Who could live here? Someone has climbed up a tree. Can you find her?

A girl and boy are playing ball. Who will catch the ball? Who will hit the ball? This girl and boy live here, too.

Find a hole in a tree. What animal could live in there?

Where is this house?

This house is in the city.

What do you see from this city window?
The houses are in a row. The walls are brick.
The brick walls are old, but they will last a
long time. Some of the city walls are painted.
They look new.

A boy and girl are playing catch.

Do you see the dog running after the ball?

The dog would like to catch the ball.

Find the boy who is running.

Can you tell why he is running?

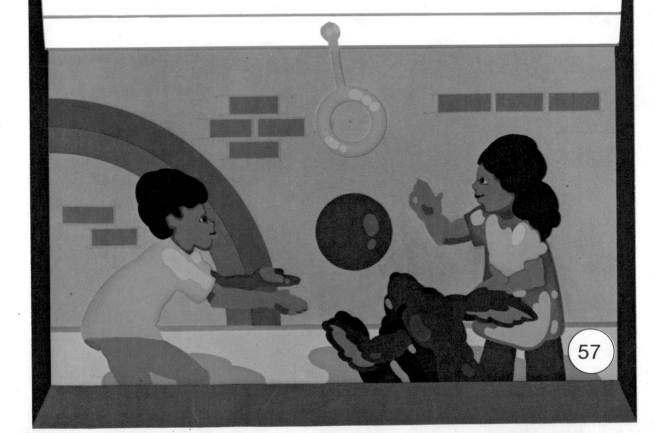

This place is flat.

The sand goes on and on.

Look at the sun. It is about to set.

The sun makes the sand look pink.

What is this girl doing?

Find something lying in the sun.

58

Do you ever look out the window?

Can you see trees?

Do you ever see an animal playing?

Have you ever seen the sun set?

What things do you see day after day?

Look out your window.

Look for something old.

Look for something new.

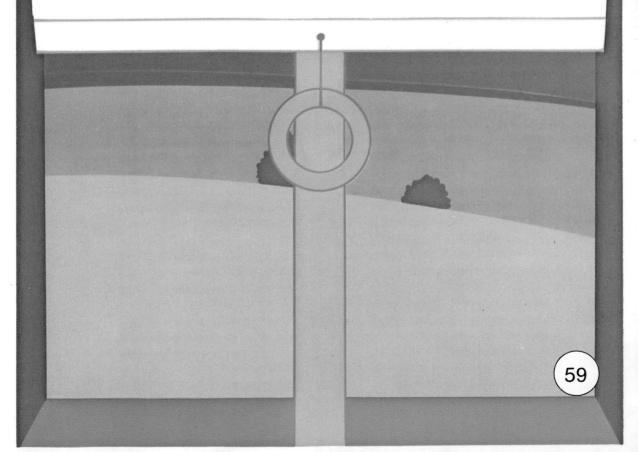

Sea Frog, City Frog

Dorothy Van Woerkom

Sea Frog lived in a bog by the sea.

City Frog lived in a pond in the city.

One day Sea Frog said, " How nice it would be to see the city! "

City Frog said, " I would like to see the sea! "

So City Frog jumped out of his pond.

He hopped down the road to the sea.

Sea Frog jumped out of his bog.

He hopped up the road to the city.

The two frogs hopped for a day and
a night. At last they came to a hill.

Up one side of the hill hopped City Frog.
How tired he was!

Up the other side of the hill hopped
Sea Frog. He was tired, too!

The two frogs met at the top of the hill.

" Hello ! " said City Frog.

" I am from the city. I am going to the sea. "

Sea Frog said, " I am from the sea, and I am going to the city. "

" How nice that we should meet, " said City Frog. " Let us rest and talk. "

" It would be nice to be tall, "
said City Frog.

" We can make ourselves tall, "
said Sea Frog. " Like this. " Sea Frog
stood up with his front legs in the air.

Then City Frog stood up on his hind legs.

" I can see a long way ! " said City Frog.

" So can I, " Sea Frog said.

So City Frog turned his nose to the sea.

Sea Frog turned his nose to the city.

The poor, silly frogs!

Their noses were turned

where they wanted to go.

But their great eyes—

which were at the back of their heads—

only saw where they had been!

" Oh, my ! " said Sea Frog.

" The city is just like the sea ! "

" Dear me ! " said City Frog.

" The sea is just like the city ! "

So the frogs went home again.

They never knew that the sea

is not at all like the city,

and the city is not at all like the sea.

67

A New House

Arnold Lobel

The road went up a steep hill.
Grasshopper climbed to the top.
He found a big apple lying on the ground.
" I will have my lunch, " said Grasshopper.
He ate a big bite of the apple.

" Look what you did! " said a worm,
who lived in the apple.
" You have made a hole in my roof! "

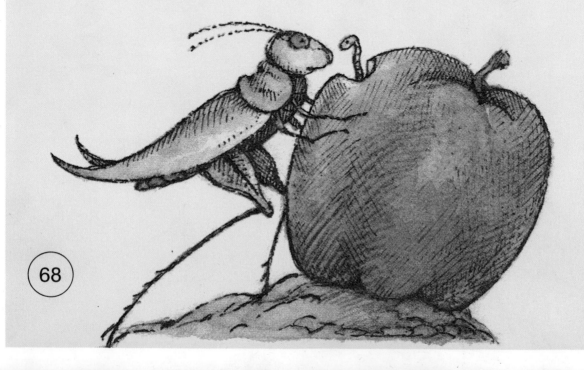

" It is not nice to eat a person's house, "
said the worm.

" I am sorry, " said Grasshopper.

Just then the apple began to roll down
the road.

" Stop me! Catch me! " cried the worm.
The apple was rolling faster and faster.

" Help, my head is bumping on the walls!
My dishes are falling! " cried the worm.

Grasshopper ran after the apple.

" Everything is a mess in here! "
cried the worm.

" My bathtub is in the living room.
My bed is in the kitchen! "

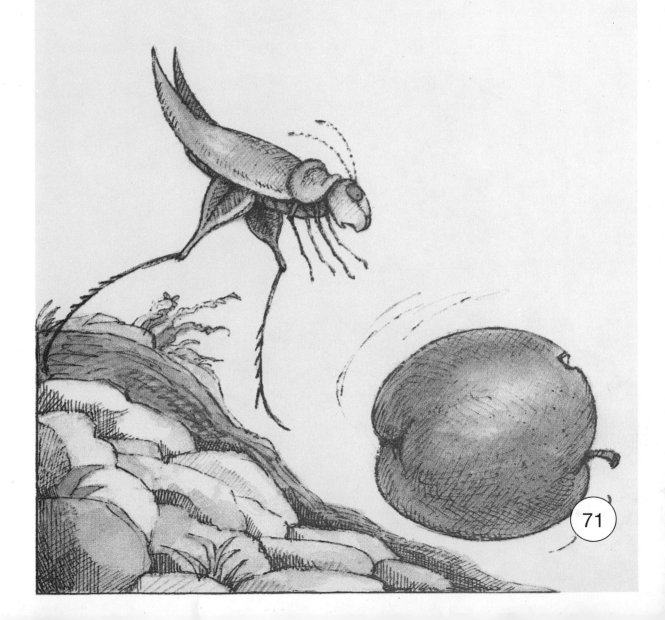

Grasshopper kept running down the hill.
But he could not catch the apple.

"I am getting dizzy," cried the worm.
"My floor is on the roof! My roof is on
the floor!"

The apple rolled and rolled.
It rolled all the way down to the
bottom of the hill.

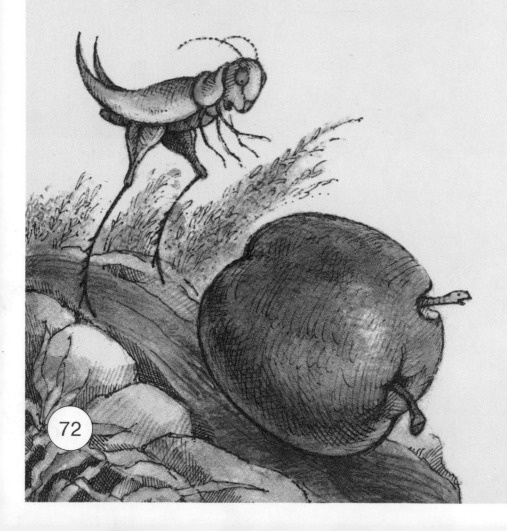

The apple hit a tree.

It smashed into a hundred pieces.

"Too bad, worm," said Grasshopper.

"Your house is gone."

The worm climbed up the side of the tree.

" It was old, " said the worm.

" It had a big bite in it anyway.

This is a fine time for me to find

a new house. "

Grasshopper looked up into the tree.
He saw that it was filled with apples.
Grasshopper smiled, and he went on
down the road.

Where Do Animals Live?

Suzanne Higgins

You know that a home has a roof and walls.
But a home is not just a roof and walls.

A home is a place to get out of the cold.
It's a place to eat. It's a place to sleep at night.

Just like you, animals need homes, too.

You read about a worm who lived in an
apple. An apple is not a real home for a worm.
Now you will read about some real
animal homes.

Have you ever seen a bird as she
hopped on the ground? The bird may be
looking for something to eat.
She may be looking for something for her nest.
A bird likes to live in a tree.
Sometimes, in the city, a bird will
make her nest on the roof of a house.

Where does a turtle live?

Maybe you have seen a turtle on the ground.

Have you ever seen a turtle lying in the water?

A turtle can make his home on the ground and in the water.

How is a turtle like a frog?

A frog and a turtle can live in the water and on the ground.

A new frog is like a fish.
.He must stay in the water.

You may have seen a little frog as he hopped out of the water.

Then you may have seen him hop back in again.

This may be his very first time out of the pond.

A fox lives in a den.

The fox must dig a hole in the ground to make her den. She will make her den away from the city.

The fox must find a place where there is running water.

When the fox has found something to eat, sometimes she will take it to her den.

A bear is like a fox in some ways.
The bear lives in a den. She will live in a
place away from the city. She will want to

be where there is running water.

A bear is not like a fox in all ways.

When it is very cold, a bear does not eat at all.

She will stay in her den and sleep.

She will sleep all day and all night.

The bear will come out when it is warm again.

She will come out to look for something to eat.

Just like you, animals need homes, too.

Have you ever seen an animal home?

What animal homes have you seen?

Who Likes What?

This is Cindy

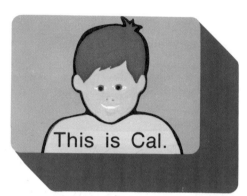

This is Cal.

cereal

city

car

cat

carrots

mice

Find a Home for All the Animals

What Do You

There are lots of ways to say something.
You can tell it. You can show it.
You will read about:
    a frog and a toad who are great pals,
    a place where a hen talks like a duck.
    First, you will find out about a new way
to talk to someone.

87

Click! Click! Stan Goodman

"Lou, look at the new toy I got," said Joan. "It's a walkie-talkie."

"Joan, do you and Lou want to go to the store with me?" asked Mom.

"Lou, do you want to go to the store?" asked Joan.

"OK," said Lou. "Maybe we can take your walkie-talkie with us."

Mom said, " I have to get some things.
I'll meet both of you here in a little while. "

" OK, Mom, " said Joan.
" We'll both be here. "

Joan gave Lou one walkie-talkie.

" Talk into the walkie-talkie, Lou, "
said Joan. " I'll see if I can hear you. "

Lou said something into the walkie-talkie.

Click! Click! " Hello, Joan. This is Lou, "
said Lou. " Can you hear me? "

Click! Click! " Yes, Lou, " said Joan.
" I can hear you, but I can hear you without
the walkie-talkie, too. You're not
far enough away. Walk away from me. "

Click! Click! " OK, " said Lou.

Lou walked where Joan could not see him.

Click! Click! " Hello, Joan. This is Lou, "
said Lou. " Can you hear me now ? "

Click! Click! " Yes, I can hear you, "
said Joan. " Lou, you don't have to say who
you are over and over. I know it's you. "

Click! Click! " OK, " said Lou.
" Joan, this walkie-talkie is great. I'll keep on
going for a while. I'll see how far I can go. "

91

Click ! Click ! " Hello, Joan, " said Lou.
" This is you know who. Can you hear me ? "

Click ! Click ! " Yes, I can hear you, "
said Joan. " Where are you ? "

Click ! Click ! " I can see some books, "
said Lou.

Click ! Click ! " Lou, you have
gone far enough, " said Joan.
" You could get lost. Come back now. "

Click ! Click ! " OK, " said Lou.

" I'm on my way. "

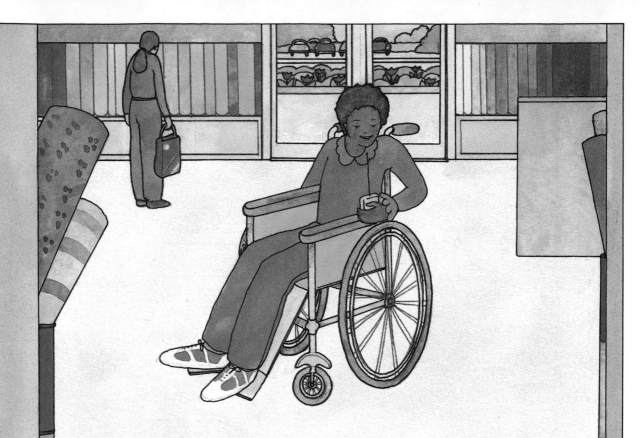

" Where is Lou ? " thought Joan.
" It should not take him this long to come back. "
Click ! Click ! " Hello, Lou, " said Joan.
" Can you hear me ? "
Click ! Click ! " I can hear you, but I
can't find you ! " said Lou.
Click ! Click ! " It's OK, Lou, " said Joan.
" I know my way around this store.
I'll help you find your way.
Tell me what is around you. "

Lou told Joan what he could see around him.

Click! Click! " I know where you are, " said Joan. " Listen to me, and you will find your way out. "

Joan told Lou where to go. Lou did

just what Joan told him to do.

Soon Joan saw Lou.

"It's a good thing we had the walkie-talkie," said Lou. "I thought it was only a toy."

"It's not just a toy," said Joan. "It helped you find your way back."

"That was fun!" said Lou.

"Fun?" asked Joan. "You could still be lost!"

"You're right," said Lou. "I think we have had enough fun for a while. We can both wait here for your mom. Over and out."

What Is a Walkie-Talkie?

A walkie-talkie is like a radio.
It is a two-way radio.
You can talk into a walkie-talkie.
You can listen to someone talking to you.
Two people can talk to
each other from far away.

Some people need walkie-talkies for the work they do. Police officers need walkie-talkies.

Why would police officers use walkie-talkies? They use walkie-talkies to find out something fast.

What other people need walkie-talkies at work?

You can make a walkie-talkie. You need two paper cups. You need some string.

First make a hole at the end of each cup. Then put some string into each hole. Tie one end of the string into one cup. Tie the other end of the string into the other cup. Tie the string tight so it won't come out.

Keep one of the paper cups.

Then give one paper cup to a friend.

Pull the string tight.

Now talk into your cup.

Have your friend listen into her cup.

Then your friend can talk,
and you can listen.

See how long you can make the string.

Don't forget to pull it tight.

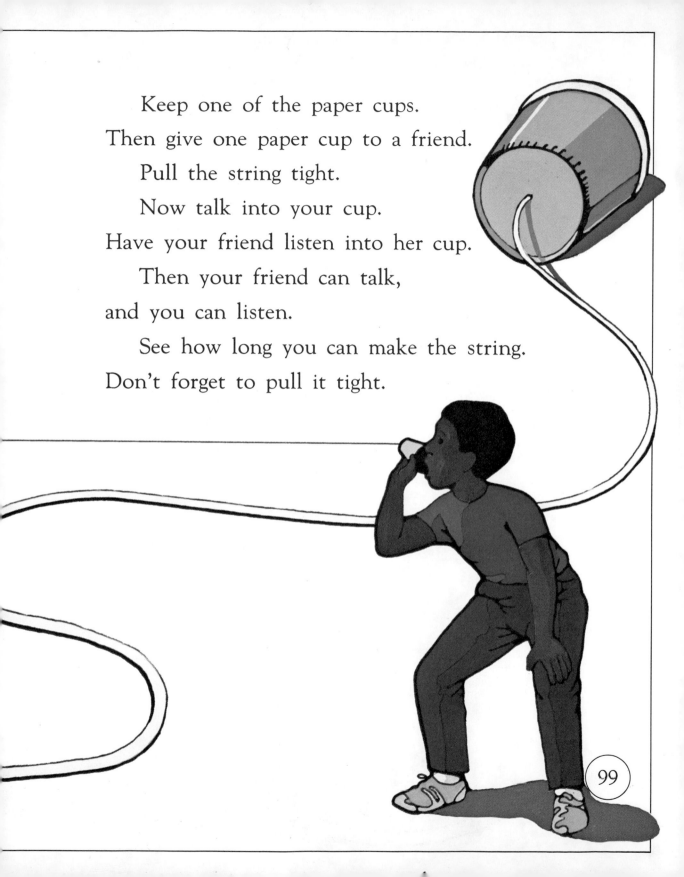

Hello Is Something You Can Show
Elaine Marcell

Lee's mom told her she would
get a surprise tomorrow.

" I don't know if I want a surprise, "
said Lee. " It's so hard to wait for one. "

" Maybe you can guess what it is, " said Dad.

Lee thought hard. Then she asked,
" Will Grandma come to stay over for a while ? "

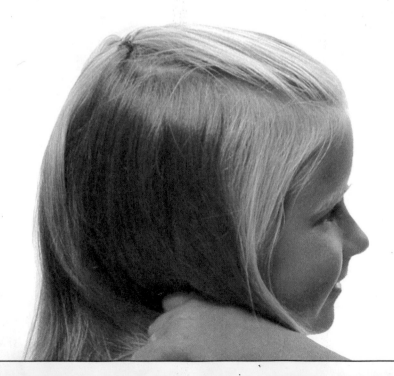

" No, " said Dad. " Guess again. "

" Is it a new toy for the yard ? " asked Lee.

" No, " said Mom. " It's not a toy. "

" I know, " said Lee. " It's a frog.

Tomorrow we'll go into the woods to find one. "

Dad and Mom said, " No ! "

Tomorrow came. Lee ran into the kitchen. She looked everywhere. " Where is my surprise ? " she asked.

Mom told Lee to look out the window.

" Someone is walking across the yard with Dad, " said Lee.

" That's Lucía, " said Mom.

Lucía came into the house with Dad.

" Hello, Lucía, " said Lee.

" ¡ *Hola* ! " said Lucía.

" What did you say ? " Lee asked. " I don't know what you mean. "

" Lucía said hello, " said Mom.
" ¡ *Hola* ! is another way to say hello.
I met Lucía and her mom and dad yesterday.
They come from a place far away from here.
Lucía has come over to play with you for
a while. "

" How can she do that ? " asked Lee.
" I can't talk to her. I can't ask her
what she likes to do. "

" You will find a way, " said Mom.

103

Lee looked at Lucía. Lucía looked at Lee.

After a while, Lee said, " Let me guess what you would like to do. Would you like to see how high we can jump? " asked Lee.

Lee jumped as high as she could. Lucía did not say a thing.

" Would you like to play ball? " asked Lee.

Lucía did not say a thing.

" I don't know how to talk to you, " said Lee. " There must be a way. "

Lee thought hard.

" Maybe I can't tell you what I want to, "
said Lee. " But, I can show you. "

Lee got some paper.
She began to make something.
First, Lee made a toy train.
Then she made a ball.

Lee showed Lucía the paper.

" Look at these, " Lee said.

Lucía looked happy when she saw the ball.

" Do you want to play ball in the yard ? " asked Lee.

Lucía began to make something on the paper. Lee looked at what Lucía made.

" Now I know what you want to do, " said Lee.

Lee thought she was going to like
her surprise after all.

" We did not begin very well, " said Lee.
" Maybe we can begin again. ¡ *Hola* ! Lucía. "

" Hello, " said Lucía.

Blum

Dog means dog,
And cat means cat;
And there are lots
Of words like that.

A cart's a cart
To pull or shove,
A plate's a plate,
To eat off of.

But there are other
Words I say
When I am left
Alone to play.

Blum is one.
Blum is a word
That very few
Have ever heard.

I like to say it,
" Blum, Blum, Blum "—
I do it loud
Or in a hum.

All by itself
It's nice to sing:
It does not mean
A single thing.

Dorothy Aldis

109

The Surprise

Arnold Lobel

It was October.

The leaves had fallen off the trees.

They were lying on the ground.

" I will go to Toad's house, " said Frog.

" I will rake all of the leaves on his lawn.

Toad will be surprised. "

Toad looked out of his window.

"These messy leaves have covered everything," said Toad.

"I will run over to Frog's house. I will rake all of his leaves. Frog will be very pleased."

Frog ran through the woods
so that Toad would not see him.

Toad ran through the high grass
so that Frog would not see him.

Frog came to Toad's house.

He looked in the window.

"Good," said Frog. "Toad is out.

He will never know

who raked his leaves."

Toad got to Frog's house.
He looked in the window.

" Good, " said Toad.
" Frog is not home.
He will never guess
who raked his leaves. "

Frog worked hard.

He raked the leaves into a pile.

Soon Toad's lawn was clean.

Frog picked up his rake and started home.

Toad pushed and pulled on the rake.
He raked the leaves into a pile.
Soon there was not a leaf in
Frog's yard. Toad took his rake and
started home.

A wind came.

It blew across the land.

The leaves that Frog

had raked for Toad blew everywhere.

The leaves that Toad

had raked for Frog blew everywhere.

At home, Frog said, " Tomorrow
I will clean up my own lawn.
How surprised Toad must be ! "

At home, Toad said, " Tomorrow
I will rake all of my own leaves.
How surprised Frog must be ! "

That night Frog and Toad were both
happy. They each turned out
the light and went to bed.

What Does a Pig Say?

James Hook

" It's time we had a hen, " said the farmer.

" Yes, " said Patsy. " I guess we could use
a fat red hen. "

So Patsy started to town to find a hen.
She came back with a hen, a fat red hen.

" What a nice hen we have ! " said the farmer.
" We need a fat red hen that says *Cluck Cluck.* "

But the hen didn't say, " Cluck Cluck. "
She said, " Quack Quack. "

QUACK
QUACK

" Cluck Cluck, " said the farmer to the hen.

" Quack Quack, " said the hen to the farmer.

" Well, " said the farmer, " this can't be—
a hen that talks like a duck ! "

" Maybe we need a duck that says
Quack Quack, " said the farmer.

" Yes, " said Patsy. " I guess we could use
a soft white duck. "

So Patsy started on her way to town to
find a duck. Back she came with a duck,
a soft white duck.

" What a nice duck we have ! " said the farmer.
" A farm needs a soft white duck that
says *Quack Quack.* "

But the duck didn't say, " Quack Quack. "
He said, " Oink Oink. "

OINK
OINK

" Quack Quack, " said the farmer to the duck.

" Oink Oink, " said the duck to the farmer.

" Well, " said the farmer, " this can't be—
a duck that talks like a pig ! "

Now the farmer didn't know what to do.
" Maybe we need a pig that says *Oink Oink,* "
he said.

" Yes, " said Patsy. " I guess we could use
a big, big pig. "

So one last time,
Patsy started on her way to town.
Back she came with a pig, a big, big pig.

" What a nice pig ! " said the farmer.
" A farm needs a big, big pig that
says *Oink Oink.* "

But the pig didn't say, " Oink Oink. "
She didn't say a thing.

The hen said, " Quack Quack. "
The pig didn't say a thing.

Then the duck crept up to the pig and said,
" Oink Oink. "
That was enough for the pig!
That was all she could take.

The big, big pig did not say one little Oink.
She said three big ones!
OINK! OINK! OINK!

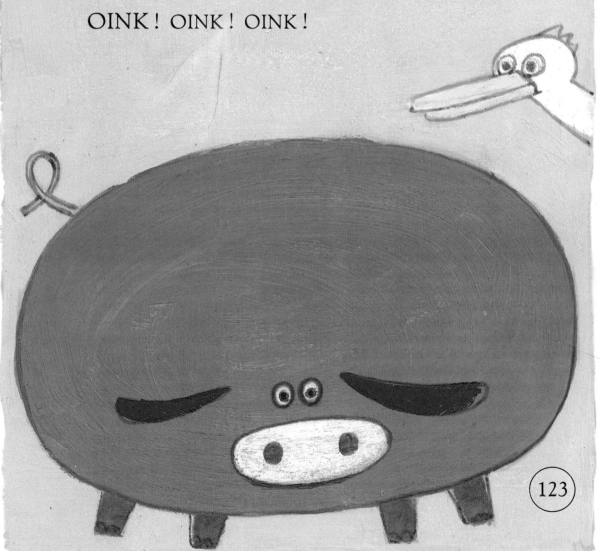

Then the duck looked at the hen and said,
" Quack Quack. "

The hen looked at the farmer and said,
" Cluck Cluck. "

" Well, well, " said the farmer.

" My, my, " said Patsy.

What Made It Happen?

Th

Here are some old tales and some new tales.
You will read about:
    a chick who forgets,
    a place where there are blue trees,
    someone who plays some tricks.

Let's begin with a rabbit you may know.

at's
the Way It Happened

127

Who Is Beatrix Potter?

Nancy Baron

Do you know this rabbit?
That's right! It is Peter Rabbit.
You may know the story of *Peter Rabbit*.
Do you know who wrote this story?
Beatrix Potter wrote *Peter Rabbit*
a long time ago.

Beatrix Potter did not write *Peter Rabbit*
as a book. She wrote the story in a letter.
The letter was for a little boy who was sick.

The letter that Beatrix Potter wrote began like this:

The letter told the story of *Peter Rabbit*.
Do you know the rest of the story?
Do you know what happened to Peter?

129

Do you know this squirrel?
This is Squirrel Nutkin. Is Nutkin
a good name for a squirrel?

Beatrix Potter wrote a story about
Squirrel Nutkin. Do you know how he lost
some of his tail? You can find out if you
read the story about Squirrel Nutkin.

Beatrix lived in the city some of her life.
She lived on a farm some of her life, too.
Beatrix looked for animals everywhere.
She liked to draw the animals she saw.

Beatrix Potter had a lot of her own pets.
One of her pets was a hedgehog!

The name of the hedgehog was
Mrs. Tiggy-Winkle. Mrs. Tiggy-Winkle liked to
sleep a lot. She liked to drink tea out of
a little cup!

Beatrix Potter wrote a story about
a hedgehog. Can you guess the name of
the hedgehog?

It's Mrs. Tiggy-Winkle!

What is Mrs. Tiggy-Winkle doing?

Beatrix had some mice as pets.

Two of the mice were Tom and Hunca-Munca.

Beatrix liked to look at them play.

She wrote a book about Tom and
Hunca-Munca, too.

Oh no!

What is Hunca-Munca doing?

What animals do you
see here? Now you know
about some of them.

Beatrix Potter put all
of these animals in books.
Maybe you can find
some of these books.

135

What Is a Play?

A play is a story that you can act out.

A play tells you what to say and what to do.

You are going to read a play now.

First you will find out who is in the play.

This tells you who is in the play.

MOTHER HEN

LITTLE CHICKEN

FROG

GOAT

ROBIN

This tells you who is talking.

    <u>MOTHER HEN</u>: Chicken, I need your help.

This tells you what they say.

    MOTHER HEN: <u>Chicken, I need your help.</u>

    The play you will read now has a Storyteller.
The Storyteller will tell some of the story.

    So now you know who is in this play.
You know how to tell who is talking.
You can tell what they are saying.
Read on.

Chicken Forgets

A play adapted from the story by Miska Miles

MOTHER HEN: Chicken, I need your help.

I want you to go berry hunting.

I need a basket of blackberries.

LITTLE CHICKEN: I would like to go berry hunting.

MOTHER HEN: Take this basket and fill it to the top.
Sometimes you forget things.
THIS time, please, please keep your
mind on what you are doing.
Please don't forget.

LITTLE CHICKEN: I will not forget, Mother.
I'll get some blackberries.

139

STORYTELLER: He started on his way.
He didn't want to forget.
So he said to himself over
and over:

LITTLE CHICKEN: Get blackberries. Get blackberries.

STORYTELLER: All the way to the river
he said to himself:

LITTLE CHICKEN: Get blackberries.

STORYTELLER: Then the chicken saw an old frog.

FROG: What are you saying?

LITTLE CHICKEN: Get blackberries.

FROG: If you're talking to me, you should not say that.

LITTLE CHICKEN: What SHOULD I say?

FROG: Get a big green fly.

STORYTELLER: The chicken went on his way.

He didn't want to forget.

So he said to himself:

LITTLE CHICKEN: Get a big green fly.

Get a big green fly.

STORYTELLER: All the way to the pasture he said:

LITTLE CHICKEN: Get a big green fly.

STORYTELLER: At the pasture, the chicken saw a goat.

GOAT: If you are talking to ME, you should NOT say, get a green fly.
You should say, get green weeds.

LITTLE CHICKEN: Oh ?

STORYTELLER: And the little chicken went on his way. He said to himself:

LITTLE CHICKEN: Get green weeds.
Get green weeds.

143

ROBIN: No, no. Blackberries are best. Come with me.

STORYTELLER: So the little chicken went with the robin. He came to a beautiful patch of sweet blackberries.
The little chicken filled his basket with the beautiful blackberries.
Then he started home.
Back he went, through the pasture.
He ate three blackberries.
Back he went by the river.
And he ate three more blackberries.

STORYTELLER: At home, the mother hen looked at the basket.

MOTHER HEN: You DIDN'T forget.
You brought home blackberries.
And the basket is just about full.

LITTLE CHICKEN: It's not hard to remember when you try.

MOTHER HEN: I'm proud of you.

STORYTELLER: And the little chicken was proud, too.

The Blue Forest   Michael Barnes

Elena liked to walk in a forest near
a mountain. She knew this forest inside
and out.

One day, Elena saw that something was
not right.

The forest near the mountain was blue.
The trees were blue. The grass was blue.
A blue bird sang in a blue tree.
Blue foxes ran after a blue rabbit.

Just then Elena saw some little blue people.

" Hello, " said Elena.

" Go away! " a little blue man said.
" We have a lot of work to do. "

" Why is everything blue? " asked Elena.
" The grass and the leaves should be green. "

" We can't find the pot of green, "
said a little blue woman. " All we have is
a pot of blue, a pot of yellow, and a
pot of red. "

" We made everything red yesterday, "
said the woman. " Maybe we will make
everything yellow tomorrow.
What color would you like everything the
next day ? "

" I like blue the best, " said the man.
" Next, we will make everything blue. "
" I like yellow the best, " said the woman.
" I'd like to make everything yellow. "
" Blue is best, " said the man.
" Yellow is best, " said the woman.
" Blue ! " said the man.
" Yellow ! " said the woman.

While the man and woman were shouting,
some of the blue got into the pot of yellow.

Elena said, " Look what happened ! "
The man and the woman looked, and
they liked what they saw.

" The blue and the yellow made green, "
said Elena. " Now you can make the grass and
the leaves green. "

BLUE

151

"We did not know that blue and yellow made green," said the man.

"Why don't you mix some yellow with some red?" asked Elena. "Maybe you will make another color."

The little people put some yellow with some red.

"Look!" said the man. "We have made orange!"

" This is fun ! " said the woman.
" Is there another color we can make ? "

" You have not put the red with the blue, " said Elena.

The little people put some red with some blue.

" Look at that ! " said the man.

" We have made purple ! "

The little people were so happy.
They liked the colors they had made.
They put a little of this with a little of that.
Color was everywhere!

" Look ! " said Elena.

She was looking at something in the sky.

The little people looked up.

They saw a beautiful rainbow over the mountain.

They had made a rainbow with all the colors.

They did not know that they could make

something so beautiful.

155

How Little Lamb Fooled Señor Coyote

A Mexican tale adapted by Verna Aardema

Little Lamb lived on a farm near a mountain. She was as thin as a beanpod.

" I am too thin, " she thought.
" I must eat more hay. "

Little Lamb was about to eat some hay when Señor Coyote found her.

" Little Lamb, I'm going to
eat you ! " said Señor Coyote.

" Señor Coyote, please do not
eat me now, " said Little Lamb.
" I am as thin as a beanpod.
After I eat all this hay, I will be fat.
Then you may eat me. "

" All right, " said Señor Coyote.
" I'll come back when you are fat. "

Day after day, Little Lamb ate hay.
At last she became fat. But then she was
afraid that Señor Coyote would come back.

The next day, Little Lamb saw
Señor Coyote coming. She ran into a
cave in the mountain. She lay on her
back and put her feet on the roof of
the cave.

Soon Señor Coyote found her.

" Little Lamb, I see you in there, "
said Señor Coyote. " Come out, so I can
eat you ! "

" Señor Coyote, " cried Little Lamb,
" you can't eat me now !
I have to hold up this mountain !
If I let go, it will fall !
Will you hold it, so I can get help ? "

Señor Coyote did not want to help.
But he did not want the mountain
to fall on him. So he went into
the cave and lay down.

" Put your feet up, " said Little Lamb.
" Push hard! Do you have it now? "

" Yes, " said Señor Coyote. " But I can't
hold it long. Come back soon! "

161

Little Lamb ran away.

Señor Coyote held up that mountain
as long as he could. Then he let go.
The mountain did not fall down.

" That Little Lamb ! " he cried.

" She played a trick on me ! "

The next day, Señor Coyote came back.
He said, " Little Lamb, I'm going to
eat you now ! "

" You may eat me, " said Little Lamb.
" But, please, eat me in one big bite.
Please don't eat me bit by bit. "

" I can't eat you in one big bite, "
said Señor Coyote. " You are too big ! "

" Oh yes, you can ! " cried Little Lamb.
" Open your mouth wide. I will
run right in ! "

The silly coyote began to open his mouth.

Little Lamb put her head down.

She ran fast!

Señor Coyote looked! He saw
her hard little head coming at him.

" Help ! " he cried.

And away he ran.

From that day on, Little Lamb
lived on the farm near the mountain.
And she didn't see Señor Coyote ever again.

Can You Guess?

 I am big.

I live on a farm.

I like to eat hay.

You can ride on my back.

What am I?

 I am red.

I am yellow.

I am blue and green.

I am orange and purple, too.

After it rains, you can find me in the sky.

What am I?

Say It Another Way

We are looking for the field.

We would like to hunt for blackberries.

We'll go this way.

Don't get lost!

You're doing a great job!

We'd like to eat some now.

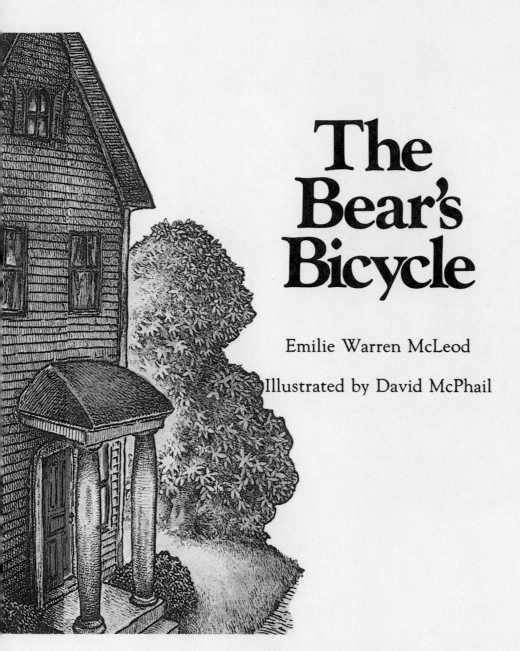

The
Bear's
Bicycle

Emilie Warren McLeod

Illustrated by David McPhail

Every afternoon we go bike riding.

I check the tires and the brakes
and make sure the handlebars turn.

Then I get on my bike and coast down
the driveway. At the end of the driveway

I look to the right and to the left.

I make the hand signal for a right turn
and I turn right.

If I have to cross the street

I stop and get off my bike.

I look both ways.

If no cars are coming

(174) I walk my bike across the street.

I stop for dogs to make sure
they are friendly.

And when I come up behind people
I warn them so they can get out of the way.

When I go down a hill I don't go too fast

and I use my brakes.

I always start home before it is dark

and put away my bike.

I wipe my feet before going in the house.

Then we have milk and crackers.

New Words in This Book

The following new words are presented in Level 6, *Across the Fence*. Words printed in regular type are new Basic words, those underlined are Enrichment words, and those printed in color are new words that pupils can decode independently.

UNIT 1

8. very
10. I'm
11. ducklings
12. flew
14. he's
15. across
    couldn't
    them
    myself
16. bones
    floor
    kitchen
    place
    getting
    mess
    dishes
    filled
    these
17. Bear
    friends
    game
    lunch
18. Dog's
    holes
    it's
    if

19. Owl
22. Bear's
    took
    them
23. forget
24. build
    plan
    builder
    makes
    wants
    picture
25. tools
    use
26. building
    brick
    stone
    wood
    things
28. seen
    ever
    only
30. clue
    Tim
    lives
    talking
31. hello
    nice

ourselves
32. which
    clues
33. tall
    air
34. knew
    road
35. silly
36. pink
    eyes
    ears
    hold
    donkey
37. birthday
    needs
38. Puff
    Sue's
    Sue
    fine
    pest
39. kissed
    top
40. kiss
    jump
42. Jack
43. Gail

44. Peg
    jumps

UNIT 2

54. window
    trees
    old
    new
    lying
55. live
    climbed
    girl
    boy
    playing
    catch
    hit
    animal
56. city
    houses
    row
    walls
    painted
57. running
58. flat
    sand
    set
59. ever

190

60. sea
    lived
    bog
61. hopped
62. frogs
    night
    hill
    side
    tired
    other
63. met
    should
    meet
    let
    rest
64. stood
    front
    legs
    hind
65. turned
    nose
    poor
    their
    noses
    heads
    been
66. dear
67. never
68. steep
    Grass-
      hopper
    apple
    ground
    ate

    bite
    worm
    roof
69. person's
    sorry
    began
    roll
    rolling
    faster
70. head
    bumping
    falling
71. bathtub
    living
      room
    bed
72. dizzy
    rolled
73. smashed
    hundred
    pieces
    bad
    gone
74. anyway
75. apples
    smiled
77. animals
    cold
    sleep
    homes
    read
78. nest
81. den
83. warm

UNIT 3
88. click
    Lou
    toy
    Joan
    walkie-
      talkie
    store
89. both
    while
90. without
    far
    enough
91. over
92. lost
94. told
95. soon
    you're
96. radio
    two
    people
    each
97. walkie-
      talkies
    police
      officers
    fast
98. paper
    cups
    string
    end
    cup
    tie
    tight

99. pull
100. show
    Lee's
    surprise
    tomorrow
    Lee
    hard
    guess
101. yard
    woods
102. every-
      where
    Lucia
    Hola
104. high
    jump
106. showed
107. begin
110. October
    leaves
    fallen
    off
    Toad's
    rake
    lawn
    surprised
111. messy
    covered
    every-
      thing
    Frog's
    pleased
112. through
    so

grass
113. raked
115. worked
pile
soon
clean
started
116. pushed
pulled
leaf
117. wind
blew
land
118. own
120. farmer
Patsy
fat
town
says
cluck
quack
talks
121. soft
oink
123. crept
ones

UNIT 4
128. Beatrix
Potter
right

Peter
story
wrote
129. write
as
letter
sick
130. squirrel
Nutkin
name
tail
131. life
farm
liked
draw
132. lot
pets
hedge-
hog
Mrs.
Tiggy-
Winkle
tea
133. mice
Tom
Hunca-
Munca
136. act
tells
Mother
Chicken

Goat
Robin
137. Story-
teller
138. forgets
berry
hunting
basket
black-
berries
139. please
mind
140. himself
river
141. should
green
142. pasture
143. weeds
144. patch
sweet
more
145. brought
full
remem-
ber
try
proud
146. blue
forest
Elena
near
mountain

inside
147. foxes
148. pot
woman
yellow
149. color
next
150. I'd
151. shouting
152. orange
153. purple
154. colors
155. sky
rainbow
157. Lamb
fooled
Señor
Coyote
thin
beanpod
hay
159. coming
cave
lay
160. fall
161. push
162. held
played
163. bit
open
mouth
wide

BCDEFGHIJO87654
Printed in the United States of America